Animal
Stories
that
Really Happened

Animal
Stories
that
Really Happened

Pat Posner

Illustrated by Peter Bailey

Scholastic Children's Books,
Commonwealth House, 1–19 New Oxford Street,
London WC1A 1NU, UK

A division of Scholastic Ltd
London ~ New York ~ Toronto ~ Sydney ~ Auckland
Mexico City ~ New Delhi ~ Hong Kong

Published in the UK by Scholastic Ltd, 1999

ISBN 0 590 11102 7

All rights reserved
Typeset by Falcon Oast Graphic Art Ltd.
Printed and bound by Bath Press, Bath

2 4 6 8 10 9 7 5 3 1

Contents

Everyone likes stories about animals. *Animal Stories that Really Happened* is a collection from around the world about real life pets or wild animals who have all done something special or amazing!

Sometimes, human characters and imagined speech have been added to help make what happens feel even more real to you – but all the stories are true.

You can find out a few interesting things about each type of animal in the *Did you know. . .?* sections at the end of each story.

I hope you enjoy reading about these very special animals.

Pat Posner

The Church Cat

"All things bright and beautiful, all creatures great and small. . ."

It was a hot summer in 1940. Faith, the pretty tabby and white cat, who belonged to the vicar of St Augustine's Church in the city of London and lived with him in the vicarage next door, should have been outside in the sun. But, instead, she'd made her way into the church.

Now, she purred happily from her secret place under one of the pews. She often curled up there during church services. She liked to hear the hymns being sung and she probably liked the coolness of the church when it was so hot outside.

Some of the churchgoers knew about Faith's secret place. Often, one of them would wiggle their fingers over the edge of the pew to attract the little cat's attention. Sometimes, Faith pawed gently at the wriggling fingers; other times, purring louder than ever, she'd come out from under the pew to greet her friends. She'd jump nimbly up on to the nearest lap for a cuddle and stroke, then she'd move along to the next lap.

It had been known for one of Faith's friends to slip her a piece of bacon rind or a morsel of ham. That wouldn't happen very often now. It was wartime and the ships that had once brought food into the country were needed to carry guns and soldiers to war. There was a shortage of sugar, butter, bacon and ham. These foods were rationed; people could only buy a very small amount each week. There probably wouldn't be any to spare for Faith.

But Faith needn't have worried after all. The churchgoers still brought her titbits. Not bacon rind or ham but tiny, crispy squares of bread that had been fried in bacon fat.

Faith was always ready to eat something tasty. One morning, towards the end of August, Reverend Ross put Faith's dish of breakfast down on the kitchen floor as usual, and called, "Breakfast, Faith. Come on, Puss!" But to his surprise no furry bundle hurtled into the kitchen.

He called again; then, feeling a bit worried, he started to look for Faith. He heard a small miaow coming from under the table. He lifted a corner of the red tablecloth that hung down over the sides of the table and there, in the middle of a pile of old newspapers, was his pretty tabby and white cat and. . .

"And a kitten!" gasped Reverend Ross. "A tiny, black and white kitten!"

Faith miaowed proudly and moved

her front leg so the vicar could stroke her tiny daughter.

When he'd finished admiring the kitten, Reverend Ross poured some milk into Faith's saucer. Then he went to fetch an old basket he remembered seeing in the bottom of a cupboard. He lined it with newspaper and a bit of old sheeting. Faith purred happily as she lapped her milk and watched what her master was doing.

When she'd licked the saucer clean, she picked her kitten up in her mouth and carried it to the basket. "*It will make a really cosy bed for my kitten*," she miaowed.

At least, that's what Reverend Ross guessed Faith was telling him!

And it looked as though he'd guessed correctly. For the next few days Faith seemed to be really happy about leaving her kitten in the basket while she hurried down the three flights of stairs to go outside into the garden for a short while.

The kitten's eyes weren't open yet. Sometimes when Faith left her she cried loudly and wriggled round the basket trying to find her. Then the vicar would kneel down by the basket to stroke her and comfort her.

"You're the same colour as a panda," he whispered one day. "That's what I'll call you. Panda! And now I've given you a name, I'll have to keep you, won't I?"

Reverend Ross loved watching Faith when she returned from the garden. She did the same things every time.

First, she'd run for a quick peep into the basket to make sure her kitten was still there. Then she'd hurry to her saucer and lap some milk. After that, she cleaned her face and her paws. Then it was her kitten's turn for a wash! Panda squeaked and wriggled and waved her tiny paw in the air while Faith licked

her from
head to tail.

Finally, when
Faith snuggled down
beside Panda to feed her, two
sets of purrs would fill the kitchen.

On the morning of 6 September, Faith
became very restless. She paced the kitchen
floor miaowing anxiously. She tried to flick
drawers open with her paw, she sniffed in
every corner, she wriggled underneath the
cooker. Reverend Ross just couldn't think
what was wrong.

Then Faith ran out of the kitchen and
downstairs. "She must have wanted to go out,
that's all," murmured Reverend Ross and he

went downstairs to open the door for her.

But Faith wasn't interested in going out! She ran in and out of the downstairs rooms as if searching for something. "Must have heard a mouse under the floorboards," Reverend Ross told himself and he hurried back upstairs to finish his breakfast.

But before he had time to sit down again, Faith darted back into the room and over to the basket. Reverend Ross watched with a puzzled frown as the little cat reached in and picked Panda up.

He felt even more puzzled when Faith ran out of the kitchen and down three flights of stairs with the kitten still gripped firmly in her mouth by the scruff of its neck.

Once downstairs, Faith put the kitten inside a small alcove set into a wall where  piles of church music sheets were stored. "You silly cat, Faith! We don't want Panda down here all on her own. Come on, I'll carry her back upstairs to her basket."

Four times, Faith carried her kitten downstairs to the alcove in the wall. Four times Reverend Ross carried the kitten back upstairs. But Faith cried and a strange growling noise came from the back of her throat.

Reverend Ross sighed and, followed by Faith, went back down the three flights of stairs. Miaowing loudly, Faith watched as he moved the piles of music sheets from the alcove.

"Now, you stay here, Faith," said the vicar. "I'm going to bring Panda down in her basket and I don't want to trip over you."

He went back up for the kitten and her basket.

As soon as the vicar put the basket into the alcove, Faith climbed into it and washed Panda all over. Then, tired out by all the journeying up and down the stairs, the cat and her kitten curled up close to each other and went to sleep.

Three days later, on the afternoon of 9 September, Reverend Ross put two saucers of milk and two saucers of food on the floor close to the alcove. "I'm leaving you some extra food and milk," he told Faith. "I've got to go and see an old friend of mine who isn't very well.

He lives quite a long way away and I might not be able to get back until tomorrow morning."

That night, Faith heard a terrible sort of up-and-down wailing sound coming from somewhere outside. It was a siren to warn people that enemy planes were coming. When the siren sounded people ran to a safe place – a cellar or a special underground shelter – in case the enemy planes dropped bombs.

Faith had heard the noise two or three times before, but nothing had happened. This time, though. . .

The siren stopped wailing and the silence that followed seemed strange and eerie! Faith's whiskers twitched, the fur along her backbone stood on end, her eyes opened wider and wider. She heard feet pounding over the pavement outside, she heard voices as people called and shouted.

The people sounded worried – Faith was worried, too. She nosed her little kitten, pushing her to the very back of the basket.

There were different noises now, the sound of bombs falling on buildings. They were coming from a long way off but Faith could hear them and she didn't like them at all.

Faith lay down next to Panda. Her body was tense, her ears pricked: she felt sure something terrible was about to happen!

Then came another noise . . . it was close . . . it was moving fast . . . it sounded a bit like a train. But Faith knew it wasn't a train. She moved closer to her kitten.

There was a *terrifying* crash that seemed to go on and on and on. A bomb had hit the vicarage! The roof exploded . . . the walls exploded . . . everything around Faith and her tiny kitten shuddered and juddered and shook and crashed and banged.

The glass was blown out of the windows . . . floors fell through. . . .

Faith miaowed loudly and snuggled closer to Panda.

There was a terrible *hot* sort of smell. Over the bangs and thuds and shudderings Faith heard a crackling noise. She knew what it was. It was. . .

It was *fire*! Faith yowled. Panda mewled pathetically and tried to claw her way out of the basket. Faith grabbed Panda by the scruff of her neck then pawed and scrabbled at the tiny, trembling black and white body – pushing it underneath her.

There were hot, angry flames, falling bricks, rubble and water everywhere. Smouldering planks, hot bricks and sizzling, hissing pieces of glass fell across the recess in the wall.

Faith could see the flames, she could smell the smoke, she could feel the heat; but she stayed where she was. She *had* to protect Panda from the heat, the wet and the noise.

There was a small hole in the rubble – maybe Faith could have clambered out to safety. But for hours, she nuzzled and licked her little kitten, miaowing gently to her, trying to comfort her. Until the last part of the house collapsed to the ground.

In the morning, Reverend Ross came home and stood staring sadly at the smouldering heap of wreckage that once had been his home.

"At least nobody was inside the vicarage, Reverend!" said one of the firemen. "They wouldn't have stood a chance of surviving this!"

"But Faith and Panda were inside," said Reverend Ross. "Has anyone seen them? They might have managed to escape."

But nobody had seen

Faith or her little kitten.

Reverend Ross ran forward and started pulling and scrabbling at the piles of hot rubble. "I've got to check!" he said when the firemen told him he'd burn his hands. "I've got to see if there's any sign of my cats."

Faith recognized his voice. She lifted her weary head and miaowed urgently but huskily; her throat was sore from the smoke. Her master heard her and peered into a nearby heap of wood, splinters of glass and bricks and stones.

"I can see her!" he shouted. "I can see Faith!"

The firemen ran to help. They moved the rubble away. In the middle of it, the little alcove still stood firm and there was Faith sitting with Panda between her front paws.

Reverend Ross lifted them both out and cuddled them close to him.

Faith and Panda were alive and safe, and all because, three days earlier, Faith had been  determined to keep her kitten in that little alcove set into the wall. She *must* have known that bombs were going to fall, not just on London, but on the vicarage!

One of Reverend Ross's parishioners offered to look after Faith and Panda until Reverend Ross found somewhere to live.

★　　★　　★

"All things bright and beautiful, all creatures great and small. . ."

It was Sunday 15 September – six days after the vicarage had been bombed. As the voices lifted in song, two furry shapes purred loudly as they crept out from their secret place under one of the pews.

Faith, carrying Panda in her mouth, had followed the parishioner who was looking after them to church. Faith was still the church cat! She was something else, too. . .

Faith, the tabby and white cat, was a national heroine. She was awarded a silver medal for her "steadfast courage" by the People's Dispensary for Sick Animals. Reverend Ross hung her picture and a certificate in the tower chapel so people would never forget her bravery and her love and devotion towards Panda, her black and white kitten.

Cat Tales

The counting cat

A cat in South Africa in the 1950s gave birth to three or four litters every year. Eventually, her owners decided that the cat would only be allowed to keep one kitten out of a litter. Several times all but one kitten were taken away from the cat.

Then there came a time when the cat produced a litter of only one kitten. Her owners were delighted. But . . . six weeks later, mysterious noises were heard coming from the attic. Five well-fed kittens – the same age and size as the first kitten – were discovered! So, there'd been six kittens in the litter. Clever mum cat had hidden five of them away!

Raft-ride to Brisbane

A little cat called Minette, from Ecuador, in South America, was saved by crew members many times when she was washed overboard during a five-month and 8,560 mile long raft-ride. But when the raft landed near Brisbane, Australia, health officials seized the little black and white cat saying she must be destroyed in case she'd brought rabies with her from Ecuador. However, the captain of a Swedish cargo ship offered Minette a place on his ship and the little cat was saved.

Minette deserved her good luck because her raft-ride was part of an experiment. She'd helped prove that it had been possible for ancient man to have travelled by raft from South America to the other side of the world!

Did you know. . .?

1. Perfect pets

Cats have been popular pets for over 1,000 years. In 1887, Queen Victoria had a medal made for the RSPCA – but she sent back the first design because it didn't have a cat on it!

2. Rough and smooth

A cat's tongue feels rough because it has dozens of tiny knobs on it, which are shaped like backward hooks. The hooks are for holding food and the rough surface helps with cleaning, grooming and smoothing fur – and, it helps mothers to wash their kittens.

3. Sleepy cats

Cats spend about two-thirds of their life

asleep – that's twice as much as any other mammal. (A mammal is a warm–blooded animal that produces milk to feed its young.)

4. Listening in

Cats have sharp ears, and can hear a person coming a long time before they see them. Cats are also good at judging the tone of a voice – if they're being scolded, they quickly flick their ears anxiously backwards and forwards.

5. Purr–fect

Cats purr for different reasons, and the sounds they make mean different things. A rough purr means *"I like this . . . please don't stop!"* and a smooth purr is a sign that the cat is getting bored or sleepy.

A Boy's Best Friend

Round about the 1920s a young boy called Juan Izquierdo lived in a small house in New Mexico, USA, with his mum and dad and his grandmother. His grandmother was small and hot-tempered and thought everything in their home should be done the way she wanted. This caused a lot of arguments and made Juan feel unhappy. He hadn't got any brothers or sisters, but he did have a dog.

Old Dog, as he was called, was a Russian

wolfhound. He was very big and heavy, his coat was rough and ragged, his ears were shaped like cauliflowers and, when Juan could persuade him to walk, he moved with a limp. But Juan loved Old Dog more than anything else in the world. And Old Dog loved Juan.

Old Dog was the only thing Juan's parents and his grandmother agreed about. They thought Old Dog was a nuisance. He spent most of the time lying asleep on the floor. Their living-room was very small so they were always tripping over him. Not only that, but when he was awake, Old Dog needed feeding. The Izquierdos were poor: they couldn't afford to feed a dog who ate almost as much as two people.

One summer morning, Old Dog fell asleep in the garden. He liked sleeping out

there at this time of year. Juan thought Old
Dog probably enjoyed the smell of the
herbs his grandmother grew on their tiny
bit of land, or the scent from the distant
pine trees in the forests by the mountains.

But Old Dog was in the way again, even
though he was outside. He was lying near the
horno – the beehive-shaped outdoor oven
that Grandmother used for baking bread.

Grandmother shouted at Juan and
Juan's parents shouted at Grandmother.
Juan gently shook Old Dog and hauled him
to his feet.

"Come on, Old
Dog," he urged,
"let's go and
see William."

William lived in a ranch, just up the road. He was 11, two years older than Juan. And, after Old Dog, he was Juan's best friend.

William was grooming his horse when Juan arrived with Old Dog limping along slowly, close to his side.

"Help me finish grooming Buddy, then we'll go indoors for something to eat," said William.

Juan took Old Dog to a corner of the stables and watched the dog settle himself on the straw-lined floor.

"If it wasn't for Old Dog being so old and sleepy, I'd run away," he told William as he picked up a brush to brush Buddy's tail. "I'd cross the mountains and get a job wrangling horses over on the Pecos Wilderness."

"Spend the day here and by the time you get home the arguing will have stopped," said William. He knew how sad his younger friend felt when his grandmother was in one of her tempers.

Summer turned to winter and Juan fell sick with a cold and a high fever. Grandmother, who was very superstitious and believed in witches, hung clumps of garlic from the door handles. "That'll keep the *brujas* away," she said. After that, she helped Juan sip water melon juice, then she put raw onion slices that she'd soaked in vinegar on Juan's hot head to help the pain and bring his fever down. Doctors cost money, and if Grandmother could make Juan better, they wouldn't need the doctor.

But none of Grandmother's remedies helped. Juan got worse and his dad had to fetch the doctor after all. The doctor said Juan would have to stay in bed, or his bad cold would turn to pneumonia. In those days, pneumonia was even more serious than it is today.

Juan's parents were really worried. They were tired out from looking after Juan, fed up with stumbling sleepily over Old Dog and worried because they hadn't enough money to pay the doctor, let alone feed Old Dog.

"You ought to get rid of that great lump of a dog," Grandmother said. "Now would be a good time to do it, while Juan's too ill to stop you."

"Well, the dog *is* very old," said Juan's

dad. "And we can't afford to feed him so, maybe, having him put down would be the best thing to do."

Juan's mum nodded sadly. "I just hope Juan will understand why we had to do it," she said.

"See to it now, before you change your minds," said Grandmother.

Mr Izquierdo nodded and walked slowly over to Old Dog. He managed to heave him up and get him outside. Then he lifted the dog into the old truck he drove only when he had to.

He'd decided to take Old Dog to a friend a few miles away. The friend would do away with Old Dog!

It was a terrible day. A strong wind was blowing and sleet was falling fast. Mr Izquierdo's truck got stuck in the mud right outside the ranch where William lived.

William ran out to help. "What's Old Dog doing in the truck?" he asked in surprise. "Why isn't he with Juan?"

When Juan's dad told William he was getting rid of Old Dog, William couldn't believe his ears. Juan would be heart-broken. William wanted to dash down the road to tell his friend what was happening. But William's mother wouldn't let him go. "Juan is very ill," she said gently. "A shock like this could make him worse."

But, somehow, Juan found out. Perhaps he'd heard his parents and his grandmother talking. When his dad returned with the empty truck, Juan had disappeared!

Grandmother was in Juan's room, sobbing. The window was wide open. Even though he was so ill and weak, Juan must have found the strength to climb out of the window. Out of the window into the wind and sleet.

Mr Izquierdo went out in the truck towards the foothills to search for his sick son. Mrs Izquierdo ran to William's parents for help. They phoned for the doctor and the sheriff. William caught Buddy and rode him out over the *mesa* – the flat-topped hills – but he couldn't see his friend anywhere.

A little while later the doctor, the deputy sheriff and a friend of the sheriff's, a Native American who was a guide and knew the area well, arrived at the Izquierdos' house. Together with William, his parents and Juan's mum, they would form a search party.

Just as they were about to leave, Juan's dad drove up. He leaped out of his truck, went round to the back of it and, to everyone's surprise, lifted Old Dog out.

"My friend wasn't home when I left Old Dog at his place. I've brought him back to find Juan," he said.

He carried the heavy, sleepy dog in his arms to Juan's room and lay him down on the floor close to Juan's empty bed.

 Old Dog, who never usually woke up unless Juan woke him, got clumsily to his feet and limped over to the bed. He put his chin on the edge of it and whined pitifully.

"Old Dog, where's Juan?" said Mr Izquierdo. "Find him, boy. Find Juan."

Old Dog blundered here and there, knocking a chair over, banging into Juan's mum, whining all the time.

The guide picked Old Dog up and put him out of the window. Then he climbed out after him. "Find Juan!" he ordered.

Old Dog put his nose to the ground, sniffing for the scent of the boy he loved. He picked up the scent and moved faster. He began to run but he fell over. He whined and tried to struggle to his feet.

The guide helped him up and ran beside him, holding the thick hair on Old Dog's neck so they could run fast together.

It would soon be dark. The distant mountains – the ones Juan had said he'd cross – looked high and black, lonely and frightening, under the bleak winter sky. Old Dog, with his helper, reached the first shrub-covered foothills. The others followed, running hard.

Then Old Dog came to the river. He began to struggle across and his big clumsy feet slipped on the rocks. "He'll fall in and drown!" gasped William.

But the wily guide managed to save Old

Dog and together they crossed the river. The others followed behind. And when they got to the other side. . .

There was Juan.

His body was curled in a tight ball as he slept under a sheltering overhang of rock.

Old Dog whined and Juan woke up. Old Dog licked Juan's tears away and the doctor wrapped the cold, shivering boy in a blanket.

"I'll carry you home, son," said Juan's dad.

"No!" whispered Juan. "I don't want to go home. I can't stand all the arguing about Old Dog."

"Juan," said his dad, "I promise there'll be no more arguing."

"And Old Dog can stay," said Juan's mum.

But Juan refused to let anyone carry him home. "I'll lean on Old Dog," he said. "He'll help me and I'll help him."

In the falling darkness, Juan saw the guide nod his head and he realized that the Native American knew the thing he'd been keeping secret for years.

Old Dog, who'd searched for, and found, the person he loved with all his doggy heart, was blind!

Dog Tales

Australian Bob

On a cold winter day, in the early 1990s, Ian Doust was patrolling a remote stretch of land on his parents' property in Narooma, New South Wales, Australia. Suddenly, his motorbike tipped over and threw him off. Ian felt an agonizing pain in his leg. He couldn't move!

Ian knew he might die of cold if he had to spend the night in the open. He yelled loudly, then tried bouncing sunlight off his watch in the direction of the neighbours' place. Nothing happened so Ian started yelling again. He'd almost given up hope when Bob, his Border collie cross, turned up. Bob must have picked up his master's cries from the farmhouse a mile or so away!

Ian scrawled a note for help saying where he was and what had happened. He folded the note firmly over Bob's collar and told him to go home.

Back at the farmhouse, Bob found Ian's mum and then started whining and running around. Mrs Doust found the note around Bob's collar and rushed to the rescue. Ian was kept in hospital for a few days with a very badly broken leg. Bob probably saved his life by running home to fetch help.

A fishy dog tale!

A fisherman in Northern Siberia was upset when his dog swam across the Pechora River and vanished. Later the fisherman caught a huge pike and noticed a tail sticking out of its jaw. He cut the fish open and, barking loudly, out struggled his dog!

Did you know. . .?

1. Living together

Dogs and people have lived together for over 10,000 years – since wolves began to move into villages to look for food scraps. Wolves were trained to hunt and guard, and then to herd animals when people became farmers.

2. Faithful friend

"Fido" used to be one of the most popular names for dogs. It comes from the Latin word, *fidus*, which means faithful or trustworthy.

3. Hear this

Dogs have much more sensitive hearing than people do. You can use a special dog

whistle to call a dog – *you* can't hear any noise, but the dog can!

4. A good smell
Dogs also have a greater sense of smell than humans. They can tell who's been in their garden by the scent the animal or human left behind.

5. Big and little
The tallest dog in the world on record is a Great Dane who stood at 105.4 cm. Other tall breeds of dog include the Irish wolfhound and the borzoi. Two of the smallest breeds are the chihuahua and the Yorkshire terrier. The smallest dog on record is a Yorkshire terrier who was only 9.5 cm long and 6.3 cm high – matchbox sized!

Duckling Dilemma

It was the end of April when the female duck started to build a nest in a dense clump of grass under a bush close to the big ponds in Sydney's Royal Botanic Gardens. She stamped on the grass to flatten it, then scraped out a hollow in the middle. Then, between taking a few trips to one of the ponds to swim around and dabble for food, she collected dozens and dozens of leaves and feathers and lots of long stalks of grass to line her nest. On top of these she spread a layer of soft duck down she'd pulled from her own chest.

A few nights later, she laid her first bluey-green egg. After that, she laid one egg a day for the next six days. Then she settled down to hatch them. Early in the mornings or in the dusky evenings, she covered the eggs with feathers and leaves and went for a quick swim and a dabble for food, but she never stayed away from her nest for long.

Almost a month went by and then. . .

Cra-a-ack! *Cra-a-ack*! Her first duckling was hatching out of his egg. Then the other eggs began to crack and, before long, there were seven little ducklings lying in a jumble among the broken shells.

The bird-spotter, who'd been keeping a secret watch, smiled. *Seven* ducklings! This was a lucky year for Mother Duck. It wasn't often that *all* the eggs hatched!

Mother Duck cleared the bits of shell away and waited for the ducklings' feathers to dry. And the ducklings stretched and wriggled and made funny little chirping noises.

The duckling who'd been the first to pop out of his egg was more adventurous than his brothers and sisters. He kept trying to clamber out of the nest.

"I'll call that duckling Jonathan, after my little nephew who's always trying to climb out of his cot," the bird-spotter said to himself. He guessed that this particular duckling would always want to be doing things on his own. He'd always be somewhere behind, or some-where in front of the younger ducklings.

Sure enough, an hour or so later, when all the ducklings' feathers were dry and fluffy, Jonathan hopped right out of the nest. Mother Duck gently pushed his brothers and sisters over the edge of the nest. Then she jumped out herself and watched as the six ducklings got themselves on to their big, flat feet. Jonathan, of course, was *already* on his feet. He was wobbling about and 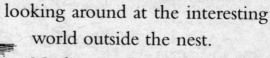 looking around at the interesting world outside the nest.

Mother Duck quacked loudly

and began to waddle away. She knew the ducklings would follow her. Six of them followed straight away. Jonathan took a bit longer. *He'd* been watching an insect crawling up a blade of grass!

When they reached the pond, six little ducklings followed Mother Duck into the water. Jonathan plopped in a couple of minutes later. *He'd* been watching a feather blowing in the gentle breeze.

After a short swim – and the occasional ride on Mother Duck's back – the ducklings began to feel tired. Mother Duck led them out of the pond and back to the nest.

Jonathan was the last one back. He'd dawdled behind, still looking about at the interesting world around him.

A few days later, on 30 May, when the bird-spotter took his usual lunchtime trip to the Royal Botanic Gardens to check on the duck family, he couldn't see them anywhere! They weren't in their nest, they  weren't on the ponds, they weren't in any of the flower-beds. Where could they be?

The bird-spotter got his answer next day when he was reading the newspaper. There was a story about a duck leading seven ducklings across four lanes of busy traffic near St Mary's Cathedral. The  ducks could have so easily been killed but, luckily, a man had leaped out of his car and stopped the traffic until the duck and her brood had made it safely to Hyde Park.

"Mother Duck must have been worried that the big eels who live in the ponds might attack her ducklings," said the bird-spotter. "It's the only reason I can think of for her moving to a new home." He shook his head when he thought about the dangerous journey.

"Mother Duck must have led the ducklings through the gardens and out of the Woolloomooloo gates. Then they'll have waddled along Art Gallery Road towards the hospital and the cathedral before trying to cross the road! I expect they made their way to the Pool of Remembrance once they were in Hyde

Park. I'll go and have a look at lunchtime."

At around two o'clock, the bird-spotter was on Park Street when he saw Mother Duck trying to lead the seven ducklings down a slippery slope to a footpath below. She was quacking loudly – telling her ducklings to "Hurry up!"

And, at last, they started to follow her. At least, six of them did.

"Oh, no!" groaned the bird-spotter.

"Jonathan's dawdling way behind, looking about at everything!"

And the next second ... Jonathan had completely disappeared!

The bird-spotter heard a distant quack from somewhere deep down. He ran to the top of the slope and started searching, trying to work out where the quack had come from.

Then he saw a pipe going down into the ground. And, when he knelt down he could see Jonathan right at the bottom of the pipe. He put his arm down, but he couldn't reach the duckling!

By now, a few passers-by had joined the bird-spotter. "What on earth can I do?" the bird-spotter asked them. "If I fetch a length of rope and try and wind it round the duckling, it might get round his neck and choke him."

Somebody passed him an umbrella. Maybe he could hook the duckling out with the curved handle? But, no. Jonathan was still out of reach!

Then someone had a brilliant idea! "Let's fetch some water from the Archibald Fountain. We can pour it down the hole and as the hole fills up with water, the poor little duckling will float to the top!"

The little group of rescuers used all sorts of things for fetching water from the fountain – rubbish bins, cups, plastic bags, lunch boxes. While the rescuers were hurrying to the fountain to fetch the water, and back to the hole to fill

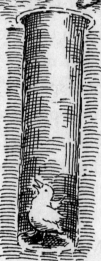

it up, Mother Duck and the six ducklings waddled around quacking anxiously.

And as the water rose in the pipe, so did Jonathan! The bird-spotter lifted him out and put him down next to Mother Duck.

A park workman arrived. He gathered all seven ducklings together in a big bin and took them to the Pool of Remembrance. Quacking louder than ever, Mother Duck followed, half-waddling and half-flying all the way to the pool.

The garden rangers from the Royal Botanic Gardens didn't know what had happened until they read about it in the newspaper next day. Then one of them went to the pool in Hyde Park to fetch the duck family back to where they belonged! A small crowd gathered round the Pool of Remembrance, watching as the ranger tried to coax the ducklings out with pieces of bread. Then the park workman came along with a long-handled scoop and the big bin he'd used the day before.

One by one, he scooped the ducklings up. One of them was much harder to catch than the others. That was Jonathan, of course!

But, at last, Jonathan was scooped up and put in the big bin with his brothers and sisters.

Then the ranger showed Mother Duck the bin with her ducklings in. "I'm taking them back to the ponds in the Royal

Botanic Gardens," he said.
And everyone cheered as
he hurried away.

The bird-spotter smiled. It was good to
think Jonathan and his brothers and sisters
were going back to the place they were
born. He glanced at Mother Duck. He
guessed it wouldn't be too long before she
made her own way back to her brood.
And, hopefully, she'd decide to bring her
family up in the Royal Botanic Gardens
after all.

 *Duck Tales*

Copy duck?

Seven years after Jonathan's duckling adventure in Sydney, a London duck and her ducklings caused chaos when they waddled into Downing Street where the Prime Minister lives. Policemen from the Prime Minister's Special Protection Group popped the duck and her ducklings into their helmets and took them back to their home in St James's Park.

The Freiburg duck

One night in Freiburg, Germany, during the Second World War, citizens were woken by a loud quacking as a very frightened duck ran through the streets. There'd been no siren warning of an air raid but, because of the duck's panicky behaviour, people dashed to their air raid shelters. Soon after, the city was heavily bombed. The survivors were so grateful to the duck they erected a monument in memory of her warning on that night!

Did you know. . .?

1. About ducklings

A mother duck usually has between eight and twelve eggs in a clutch, but she only lays one egg each day. But so that her ducklings all hatch at the same time, she doesn't begin to sit on her eggs to keep them warm (or incubate them) until the last egg is laid. When a duckling hatches from its egg, it is able to feed itself and to swim almost at once. A mother duck won't feed her young, but she will lead them to where food can be found.

2. Ducks on the move

Ducks are great travellers – they might fly thousands of miles throughout their lives!

Some ducks even spend most of the year moving in flocks from place to place. Ducks will migrate to other countries to escape from cold weather, or find good supplies of food and rain.

3. Table manners

When a duck dabbles in mud, its tongue sucks water into its bill. Bits of food stick to special plates inside the bill, and as the water swishes out, the duck can swallow the food.

4. Friends and foes

Male ducks are called drakes. If two drakes meet when there is a female duck near by, both of them pretend to drink. This is their way of telling each other that they don't want to fight. When the female duck

chooses her mate, she nods at him, and then won't let any other drake come near her.

5. Water off a duck's back

Feathers are important for flying, but they also keep ducks warm and dry. Ducks spend a lot of their time preening their feathers to keep them clean. They also spread a special oil into their feathers which keeps them waterproof. That's why water runs off a duck's back so easily.

A Very Special Pony

More than eight kilometres off the coast of Virginia, USA, lies an island with beautiful beaches, miles of water, sand dunes, woodland trails and marshy areas where salty marsh grasses grow. The island is called Assateague – its name comes from an Indian word meaning "across the marshy place".

Wandering freely on this beautiful island, feeding on leaves of stunted trees and bushes and marsh grasses, drinking fresh water from the ponds and potholes, is a herd of wild ponies – some solid brown and some with brown and white patches. They're known as the ponies of Assateague. But how did they get there in the first place?

The most popular belief is that the first ponies to live on the island swam ashore when a Spanish galleon was shipwrecked off the coast of Assateague during a terrible storm some time in the 1600s.

The ponies made the island their own – learning how to find food and drink in all weathers, even in the snowy, icy winter weather. They grew strong and had foals and the herd got bigger. The foals grew up and had foals of their own.

If there were too many wild ponies on Assateague, their food supply would run out. So every year, on the last Wednesday of July, the Volunteer Firemen of

Chincoteague, the neighbouring island, swim across the shallow bay at slack tide, round up the ponies, drive them into the water and across to Chincoteague for Pony Penning Day.

And, on Pony Penning Day, thousands of people from all over America go to Chincoteague's Carnival Grounds to see, and to buy, the wild ponies. The ones that aren't sold are driven back to Assateague.

In the summer of 1946, a Chincoteague man, known to everyone as Grandpa Beebe, bought a mare and her tiny girl foal.

Pony Penning Day was almost over when a writer called Marguerite Henry saw the little foal. She told Grandpa Beebe she wanted to write a book about an Assateague pony. She knew this beautiful filly with her silvery tail and mane, golden eyelashes and bright brown eyes was the one she wanted to write about.

"If you'll sell her to me, I'll send her back to you when she's old enough to be a mother herself, so her babies can be real Assateague ponies, too," the writer promised.

Grandpa looked at the little foal who was nuzzling into the writer's hand.

"Well. . ." he said at last, "I'll let you buy her so you can write stories about her, but she'll have to stay here for a few months, until she's old enough to leave her mother."

So, a few months later, Grandpa Beebe sent the foal to Illinois – to Marguerite Henry. Marguerite called the pony Misty and started to write her book.

The book – called *Misty of Chincoteague* – was a huge success. Misty became a celebrity and, over the next few years, was invited to horse shows, libraries, schools, bookshops and parties!

Then the time came for Misty to go back to Grandpa Beebe's ranch, to be with the other Assateague ponies and, perhaps, to have a foal of her own.

And, a year after Misty had gone back, her first foal was born. It was a colt – a boy foal. All across the country, newspapers and television and radio stations broadcast the news about Misty and her colt, Phantom Wings.

Before long, the book Marguerite Henry had written was made into a film. Misty took part in the film as one of the wild horses. She enjoyed being a celebrity again, and having lots of people petting her.

When the film-makers had finished making the film, life returned to normal for a while. But then, early one morning in 1962, something happened. . .

 The people of Chincoteague were woken up by a torrential rainstorm. They looked out of their windows and saw that the water was so high it was lapping against the sides of their homes. And it was getting higher by the minute!

By the afternoon, the raised path to the mainland was under water. Chincoteague was cut off. Then an announcement came over the radio! The people living there would have to leave. Helicopters would fly them to safe places on the mainland.

Everyone was worried about their

animals; there would be no room in the helicopters for them! Grandpa Beebe was especially worried about Misty, who was due to have another foal any time now.

"We'll have to bring her into the house, Grandpa," said one of his grandchildren. "It's lucky the house is on a small hill, the floor's still dry. We'll pile hay in one corner of the kitchen, we'll fill the sink with water and. . ."

". . . And leave her plenty of food," said Grandpa, tipping all the vegetables they had on to the floor.

So, Grandpa led Misty into her temporary home. "You'll be all right, girl," said Grandpa. "We'll be back as soon as possible, I promise," he added, before hurrying out to the waiting helicopters.

The storm had done terrible damage:

boats had been lifted out of the water and thrown on to land; some of the houses had been swept out to sea.

But the Beebes' house was still there. And Misty was safe and well. She'd eaten all the vegetables and drunk all the water from the sink and, somehow, she'd managed to open the fridge door and tip over a bottle of molasses – her favourite treat!

Early the following morning, Misty's foal was born. A little tan and white filly. The Beebes all agreed on a name for the girl foal straight away. She just had to be called Stormy.

Not all the ponies had been as lucky as Misty. Some of them had drowned and, over on Assateague, more than half of the wild pony herd had been swept out to sea.

"Just think of all the ponies sold over the years on Pony Penning Day," said a friend of Grandpa's. "If we had the money, we could buy some of them back. They'd have foals and we could build up the herd again."

A day or two later, one of the men who'd made the film about Misty phoned the Mayor to ask if the people of Chincoteague were all right after the terrible storm. When the mayor told him that a lot of the wild ponies had been drowned, the film man had an idea.

"What if I get all the cinemas to show *Misty of Chincoteague* again?" he said. "I know a lot of children have only just seen the film, but Misty and her new foal could go to the cinemas, too. That'd make everyone go again. Then, all the money the film makes can go towards buying back some of the ponies."

For three months, Misty and Stormy went from town to town, from cinema to cinema. In each cinema, they went up on to the stage so the boys and girls could speak to them and stroke Misty. Stormy was too shy to let the children stroke her, but she stood by, watching timidly.

By the end of the tour, enough money had been raised to buy back about 50 ponies. Misty, her daughter Stormy and the boys and girls from across America had saved the wild herd of Assateague.

Misty certainly turned out to be a very special pony. In 1990 a special Misty of Chincoteague Foundation was set up. Volunteers set to work raising funds to save as much as possible of the land on Chincoteague Island where Misty and Stormy once lived. And the Foundation hope, one day, there will be a museum on the island of Chincoteague. A museum dedicated to the history of the wild Assateague ponies and, of course, to that very special pony – Misty of Chincoteague.

 *Horse Tales*

Moonflower the bad-tempered horse

You've heard of guide-dogs but what about a guide-horse?

Moonflower was a bad-tempered horse who kicked and bullied the other horses living at the Pony Rescue Centre. One day, a blind pony called April arrived. Everyone was worried when Moonflower whinnied loudly and galloped up to the new arrival before they could stop her.

But they needn't have worried. Moonflower nuzzled the blind pony all over, she blew softly into her ears and then she licked the pony's blind eyes! From then on, Moonflower and April spent all their time together. Moonflower became April's eyes and guided her everywhere. Every meal-time she led April to the feeding trough and made sure the blind pony had something to eat. And if ever April seemed to be straying into danger, Moonflower nudged her shoulder and pushed her to safety.

Guide-dogs have to be trained, but nobody trained Moonflower. She just seemed to know what to do from the second she met April.

Olga the brave

Olga, a bay mare, was based with the Mounted Branch of the Metropolitan Police Force during the Second World War. She was out on patrol in London in 1944 when a flying bomb exploded near her. The blast destroyed four houses and damaged several other buildings. Then, a plate-glass window shattered and crashed into the road immediately in front of her. Poor Olga was terrified and bolted. But her rider, PC Thwaites, managed to calm her and persuaded her to return to the scene. Brave Olga remained, standing quietly, while PC Thwaites helped the rescue parties and controlled traffic. Olga was awarded a Dickin medal for her courage in carrying out her duties.

Did you know. . .?

1. Horse families

There are four main groups of horses – ponies are the smallest. The other groups are "light" horses, which have thin legs and small bones; "heavy" or "draught" horses, which have big, sturdy bones and "feral" horses, which are wild. Altogether, there are 350 different breeds of horses.

2. Horse names

Did you know that male and female horses are called by different names? A stallion is a male horse and a female horse is called a mare. A young male horse is a colt, while a young female horse is called a filly. A foal is a baby horse, until it

is one year old, and then it is known as a yearling.

3. The oldest breed

The horse's earliest ancestor, Eohippus, lived about 60 million years ago in Europe and North America. It was about the size of a fox. As their environment changed from being marshy and wet to dry and arid, horses developed into the grazing animals we have today.

4. Tall horses

People used to measure a horse's height with their hands. Today, horses are still measured in hands, but the measurement is fixed: one hand is about 10 cm (four inches).

5. Life stories

A mother horse, or mare, is pregnant for 11 months. A baby foal is able to stand up and walk just two hours after its birth, and its legs are almost as long as they'll be in adulthood. Horses are fully grown by four years of age. The average life-span of a horse is 20–25 years – but the oldest recorded horse, Old Billy, was 62 when he died.

The Police Pig

It was a warm July morning in Germany and Elvira the sow felt restless. "Ah," said the farmer as he watched her trotting back and forth, "I think it's time to take you to your farrowing pen. There's plenty of nice fresh straw there for you to make a comfy bed."

"Is Elvira getting ready to have her piglets?" asked Trudy, the farmer's daughter, when she saw her dad guiding the plump pig into the pen.

Her dad nodded and smiled.

"Will she have them today, Dad?" Trudy asked.

The farmer looked down at Elvira. "More likely tomorrow," he said.

And, sure enough, Elvira had her litter the following day – 7 July.

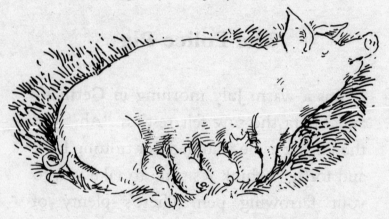

As soon as they were all born, the farmer clipped their eye-teeth with special clippers. One little she-piglet wriggled and squealed indignantly. "This one's a real character," said the farmer, laughing as the little piglet wriggled in his hands.

"Why do you have to clip their teeth?" Trudy asked anxiously.

"It doesn't hurt them," Trudy's dad smiled. "It's so they can't tear each other's faces when they scramble around to feed from Elvira." He put the piglet down and chuckled again as she shoved her brothers and sisters out of the way so that *she* could lie in the comfiest place to feed.

The lively little piglet became Trudy's favourite.

"She's the cleverest of the litter," Trudy told her parents one day, a few weeks later. "As soon as she sees me she runs up for a game. And she's been drinking milk from a saucer since she was six days old!"

A few kilometres away, at exactly the same time as Trudy was telling her parents about the "cleverest piglet", an off-duty policeman called Werner was sitting watching a cookery programme on television.

The presenter was making a very special dish using truffles. Truffles are a sort of fungus, very rare and very delicious. They grow underground in woods and forests.

"People use pigs to find the truffles," said the programme presenter. "Pigs have a highly developed sense of smell, so they're very good at sniffing out truffles."

Werner pulled his ear and looked thoughtful. He was beginning to get an idea. He decided to go and  talk to somebody about his idea straight away.

A little while later, Werner was knocking on a farmhouse door.

"Hello, Werner," said Trudy. "Have you brought your police dog with you?"

Werner shook his head. "I haven't got a dog at the moment," he said. "My dog has been retired from duty. I've come to ask if I can look at your pigs."

"OK," said Trudy, who often showed visitors around the farm. "I'll take you to see Elvira and her piglets."

Now the piglets were older they spent the daytime outside. As Werner and Trudy walked across the farmyard, Trudy shouted, "Yip-yip! Come on, girl!"

Then she smiled shyly up at Werner. "I'm calling my favourite piglet, the cleverest one of the litter," she said. "Look! That's her. The one running towards us."

Trudy reached over the metal gate of the outside pig run and scooped the piglet up. "She's ever so friendly," she said. "She's wrinkling her snout at you. I think she wants to say 'hello'. Do you want to hold her?"

Werner nodded and Trudy gave him the piglet.

"Does she always come when you call

her?" Werner asked.

Trudy nodded proudly. "I'll go over there," she said. "When I stop, you put her down and I'll call her to me."

Sure enough, when Werner put the piglet down she trotted quickly to Trudy as soon as Trudy called her.

"Will she come to me?" asked Werner.

"Call her and see," Trudy told him.

So Werner called to the piglet and she trotted quickly over to him.

"She's a real character, that one," said Trudy's father. He'd just come down from one of the fields.

"Do you think she could be trained to do the sort of work a police sniffer dog does?" asked Werner. "You know, sniffing out drugs and that sort of thing?"

"She finds bits of apple when I hide them!" said Trudy. "And she loves rootling around in the soil."

"Will you sell her to me?" Werner asked Trudy's dad. "I haven't got a dog to train at the moment. I'd like to try training this piglet instead. I've a feeling she might be even better than a dog at sniffing things out!"

Trudy held her breath. She knew they couldn't keep the piglets. She'd love her favourite one to go to Werner, then she'd be able to see her sometimes.

Trudy's dad was happy to sell the piglet to Werner. He knew the policeman would look after her well.

Werner said he'd call his piglet Luise. "And I'll bring her back to visit you," he promised Trudy, before he drove away with Luise tucked safely in a big box in the back of his car.

After a couple of days, Werner started training Luise for police work. He made up small bags filled with drugs and every time Luise touched one with her snout he gave her a reward – a nice juicy piece of apple.

One day, Werner buried some bags in his garden. "Seek, Luise," he told her. "Seek!"

Luise oinked and squealed and trotted off into the garden. She put her snout to the ground and ran along sniffing. When  she got close to the first bag he'd buried, Werner held his breath. Would Luise find it?

91

Luise stopped. She oinked twice then started rootling with her snout and trotters.

"Good girl, Luise!" Werner praised. He patted her head and gave her a piece of apple. "Now seek again!" he ordered.

Before long, Luise had found every single bag that Werner had buried.

Next day he buried some more bags. This time he buried them much, much deeper down. But, in no time at all, Luise had found them.

"It's time to let the Chief Policeman see what you can do," said Werner.

The Chief Policeman laughed when

Werner told him about Luise. "You can't be serious!" he said. "You can't possibly want to be a *pig*-handler instead of a *dog*-handler!"

But when the Chief Policeman saw how good Luise was at sniffing out drugs he agreed to let Werner have her instead of a dog!

The police dogs couldn't believe their eyes when Werner arrived for a training session with Luise. Some of them growled and raised their hackles, but Luise wasn't scared of them! Oh, no! Luise wasn't scared of anything! She faced the dogs bravely. She stood still while they sniffed her and then she sniffed them back. After that, the dogs accepted her and they all got on very well.

And the other policemen, although they had laughed at Werner's pig at first, soon began to see how clever Luise was. She often beat their dogs in training sessions – being the first to sniff out drugs and mock explosives even when they'd been buried 70 centimetres underground!

Luise soon grew big and heavy and wasn't allowed to live with Werner any more. Instead she shared a kennel with one of the police force's watchdogs – a Rottweiler called Bill.

Then came the day when Luise joined the police sniffer dogs on a *real* job. "Time to prove to everyone how good you are, Luise," Werner told her. "We're sure there are drugs hidden somewhere in this building. Seek, girl! Seek!"

 Luise looked up at Werner with her little piggy eyes and made a soft oink. Then

she was away . . . snout to the ground . . . sniff-sniff-sniffing.

Within half an hour, the sniffer pig had sniffed out hidden drugs from a dozen places!

 Next day, Luise's picture appeared in the newspaper and made everyone laugh at the thought of a pig working for the police. The Chief Policeman didn't like the newspapers making fun of the police force. He called Werner into his office.

"I'm suspending Luise from duty," he said. "She's bad for police image!"

The newspaper men got to hear about this, too. Luise's picture appeared in the newspaper again with a big headline: **Police suspend Luise from duty for being a pig!**

What an outcry *that* caused! Letters of protest arrived every day. Newspapers in other countries printed Luise's story. There was so much fuss that Luise was given her job back.

Werner was delighted. As happy as a pig with two tails! At Christmas-time, he was ordered to take Luise on a visit to the important city of Berlin, so everybody could see the clever police pig. Luise even appeared on the stage of the Hanover Opera during a special Christmas performance.

 Werner had sent Trudy and her family tickets for the performance. Trudy felt so proud when the audience cheered her favourite piglet!

In the New Year of 1985, Luise was declared an "official civil servant", working for the government. Some of the other policemen wanted to have pigs instead of dogs, but they weren't allowed to.

"You'll make history, Luise," Werner told her. "The only police pig that ever there was!"

"Oink!" Luise agreed, then she happily munched the slices of apple Werner gave her.

Luise the police pig worked for two more years. Then she retired to raise a family. And what tales of adventure she had to tell her piglets!

 *Pig Tales*

Oink-Oink!

Snort was a pot-bellied pig who lived with her owners on their converted bus in Colorado. One cold night, Snort woke up her mistress by running up and down the bus oinking loudly. Eventually, Snort's mistress realized something was very wrong. Her husband started having what looked like convulsions; she phoned for an ambulance and she found she couldn't speak properly. The couple were found to be suffering from poisoning caused by breathing in fumes from a faulty heater. If Snort hadn't oinked so loudly, her owners would probably have died in their sleep. Snort was the first pig ever to receive a life-saving award from the American Humane Association.

Another life-saving pig

Priscilla was a pet pig living in Texas. She loved having her harness and lead put on. She knew this meant it was time for a swim. One day she was swimming in Lake Somerville when a young boy in the water got into difficulties. The humans were too far away to help. Priscilla swam over to the boy who grabbed hold of her lead. He was much heavier than the three-month-old pig and kept dragging her under the water. Priscilla fought and struggled and managed to tow the boy back to shore. She won the Stillman Award for her life-saving achievement.

Did you know. . .?

1. Sniff . . . sniff

Like Luise, all pigs have a terrific sense of smell. Because they like attention from people, and they're very intelligent, they are easy to train. That's why they are often used for "sniffing out" truffles which grow underground in woods and forests.

2. About snouts

The nose, jaws and surrounding areas of a pig's head is called a snout. Pigs use their snouts for rooting up plants and bushes and, because this is like digging, pigs can help clear the land and turn the soil for farmers to grow new crops.

3. Pig lifeguards

Pigs are good swimmers. In 1898 the crew of a coastal steamer, wrecked off Sydney, were saved when their cargo of pigs swam ashore – taking lifelines with them. The crew then used the ropes to guide them to dry land.

4. What a boar!

Today's farm pigs are descendants of the wild boar who used to live in most parts of the world. They may still be found in dense forest areas over southern and central Europe. They eat roots, acorns and grubs of insects, and they've even been known to "go fishing" – taking fish from shallow ponds.

5. Helping out

In the wild, female boars roam in herds with their piglets. They help each other whenever danger threatens. Maybe this is why Snort and Priscilla, the pigs in the Pig Tales, helped when danger threatened humans.

Elephant Rescue

I'm Jodie and I'm nine. My brother Travis is 11. I want to tell you something that happened a couple of days ago. . .

Our uncle Kenneth was coming to see us. I could hardly wait! Uncle Kenneth's great. He goes on the most fantastic holidays and he shares them with us. I don't mean he takes us, though he's promised he will someday.

No, what I mean is this. As soon as he gets home from wherever he's been, he comes to see us to tell us all about it. This time he'd been on safari. Not to a safari *park* but on *proper* safari in Africa!

And, guess what! It was my turn to choose what Uncle Kenneth should tell us about first. Well, I've got a particular favourite animal. I collect ornaments and models of them; I've got over 60 different ones, and I collect posters and pictures and stories about them, and watch and record any programmes they're on.

I wondered if Uncle Kenneth would have been lucky enough to see any. . .

This is what happened when Uncle Kenneth arrived.

After he'd said "hello" to everyone, he asked me what I wanted to hear about first. Of course, I said elephants.

Uncle Kenneth smiled and said he'd hoped I'd choose elephants because he had the most amazing story to tell.

"I went on safari during the dry season," he said. "1996 was drier than usual – almost drought conditions."

I asked what it *looked* like. I was longing for Uncle Kenneth to get to the elephant part of his story, but I wanted to try and *see* the place he was talking about, to *see* what the elephants would have seen.

Uncle Kenneth nodded and said he'd stayed at a lodge in northern Namibia. It had a large and beautiful garden with lots of trees, bushes and plants. They'd all been chosen to cope with dry weather so they looked far more alive than anything in the great

 outdoors beyond. And there was a swimming-pool. . .

I said I didn't want to hear that bit. I wasn't interested in that part of it. (I didn't realize then *why* Uncle Kenneth had described the lodge's garden.) "You'll see why I mentioned the garden, later," Uncle Kenneth told me. Then he smiled and carried on. . .

"Imagine a cloudless sky, a heat haze that makes the scenery quiver, silvery mirages that look like lakes wavering above pale gold dried-up grass. The thorn trees are grey and leafless, and pools are beginning to dry up. There are still some leaves left on the baobab trees but they're a sort of dead-looking green. Food and water is scarce, the elephants travel for miles to find fresh supplies."

I asked *what* they ate. Travis looked at me as if I was stupid and said, "Everyone knows that elephants eat leaves and plants."

Uncle Kenneth winked at me, then answered my *sensible* question.

"During the dry season elephants eat bark and twigs of trees and bushes," he explained. "They use their tusks to gouge off the tough bark from thorn trees and they whittle twigs between their teeth to remove the bark. They dig for roots with their tusks and feet and they chew wild sisal leaves, too, for the moisture.

"Of course, they aren't the only animals looking for food, and anything that can be eaten disappears very quickly, which is why they have to keep moving on.

"But from mid-morning until the middle of the afternoon it's too hot for them to travel. They spend that part of the day resting in the shade of bushes and trees, flapping their large ears to help them cool down. In the early evening they start to make their way towards water."

Then, Uncle Kenneth looked at me and smiled. "I didn't actually see what happened from the *very* beginning," he admitted, "but I know enough about elephants to guess at that part of it."

I felt my toes curling up with excitement inside my trainers. I knew the *exciting* part of the story was about to start.

"It was early evening, the sun was going down and the shadows were lengthening. The elephants had been resting in the shade for a long time and one baby elephant was beginning to feel bored and restless.

"Now it was turning cooler, he was longing to get to the nearest river or water-hole. He could just imagine the sipping-squirting-spilling noises he and the other elephants would make as they stood drinking in the moonlit river.

"And mud, he thought, as he and his mum started moving. He'd be able to splosh wet, slimy mud all over himself to clean his skin. The baby elephant trumpeted happily when he thought of how he'd soon be rolling and wallowing in the mud with the other elephant calves. And of how, after that, they'd throw sand and dust on to their wet bits and then find a tree or an anthill and rub themselves against it.

"The elephant calf lengthened his stride. He got a little way ahead of his mum. She trumpeted a warning and hooked him back by thrusting one of her huge front legs under his neck, because young elephant calves shouldn't go off on their own.

"So they walked on and the baby elephant stayed close to his mum. And, at last, they came to a river. But there wasn't much water in it and already there were a lot of other elephants there.

"Mum elephant looked round. There wasn't much to eat there, either. The thorn trees had been ripped to pieces, the bushes nibbled to nothing and the grass had been grazed away to bare caked earth . . .

"She lifted her trunk. She waved it in the air, sniffing for food and water. Then the two of them trundled off on their own.

"They walked a long way. Dawn was breaking when they came to a beautiful garden. There was a building, too – they'd arrived at a lodge. Mum elephant opened the garden gate with her trunk. They went in and she stretched her trunk out to the nearest plant. It was delicious. She closed her eyes as she chewed. . .

"The baby elephant saw water. A great big shining sheet of water. He hurried towards it. His plate-like feet slipped on something smooth and shiny. He trumpeted in fright. But it was too late. *Splash-sh-sh!* He was in a huge, deep hole. It was full, *too* full, of water.

"The baby elephant trumpeted again. Louder this time. He was terrified. He didn't know how to get out of this deep hole.

"Mum elephant trumpeted back – telling her baby to swim to the edge. But the baby elephant didn't understand. Mum elephant looked round. She'd have to hurl something into the water, something her baby could climb on to. Something he could walk on until he got to the edge.

"She hurried to some garden tables and benches. One by one she hurled them into the water. But the baby elephant was frightened of them. He was *terrified* of them. He wouldn't . . . *couldn't* go near them.

"Mum looked at the trees and shrubs. The baby wouldn't be frightened of them. She called and trumpeted to him. He bellowed and trumpeted back –"

"Did you hear the trumpeting?" I asked

 Uncle Kenneth.

He nodded. "Everyone in the lodge was woken by the sound of elephants in distress. We all rushed outside into the dawn light and saw the young elephant calf in the swimming-pool. He was surrounded by all the garden furniture and the frantic elephant mum was ripping up trees and shrubs and hurling them into the pool.

"We all wanted to help. We tried to get close to the swimming-pool so we could work out a rescue plan. But the elephant mum didn't trust humans. She probably thought we wanted to hurt her baby. She ran towards us with her huge ears spread out and her trunk raised. She trumpeted loudly and fiercely, warning us off.

"By now, the baby elephant was close to drowning and all we could do was to move back and watch helplessly to see what the

114

elephant mum would do next.

"First, she paced round the edges of the pool, calling softly and comfortingly to her poor baby all the time. Then, using her tusks as levers, she started to rip up the tiles that surrounded the pool. She ripped them all up in next to no time. Then she trampled down the cement and brick sides.

"All the time her baby's calls were getting weaker. Everyone thought he was going to drown any second.

"Then, the elephant mum used her trunk and her feet to scoop earth in over the bricks and cement. She was making a ramp!

"A couple of people moved forward, they wanted to help scoop the earth. But the elephant mum trumpeted loudly and flapped her huge ears. They *had* to let her do it on her own. It would have wasted too much of her time if she'd had to keep stopping what she was doing to warn them off.

"We all thought the elephant mum wasn't going to manage in time to help her baby. But she kept on scooping earth until the ramp was made.

 "Then, trumpeting softly, she started to walk down it. Very, very slowly. Very, very carefully.

"Suddenly, the elephant calf seemed to understand what to do. Besides, his mum was closer now and he desperately wanted her, desperately needed her comfort.

"He started edging himself forward. He got his front feet on to the earth ramp. Then the elephant mum stretched her trunk out. She entwined it around her baby's trunk and hauled him to safety."

Uncle Kenneth smiled and blinked hard. "It was marvellous watching Mum elephant caress and love her baby. He stood there with his little trunk half up and half down as he tried to lift it enough to rub it against his mum. He managed in the end, and they stood for a couple of minutes or so. Then, leaving a completely wrecked swimming-pool and garden behind them, they trundled off and away. Back to the real outdoors."

I've heard and read about how well elephants care for their young, but this elephant mum was clever and determined too. People say that elephants never forget, don't they? Well, *I'll* never forget that story.

A big new word

Jumbo the Elephant, who lived at the London Zoo in Victorian times, was a great favourite with children and grown-ups alike. Soon, anything that was very big was called "Jumbo" – and a new word was added to our language.

Another Jumbo, another zoo

At a zoo in Devonshire, two elephants, Jumbo and Hosbie, kept reaching over the spiked wall of their pen with their trunks and knocking down a brick barrier some workmen were trying to build outside the pen. One workman had a brilliant idea; he'd heard that elephants were gentle towards other creatures. "Let's put white mice on the flat bits between the spikes. The elephants won't want to reach over the spiked wall with their trunks in case they hurt the mice." It worked. The elephants saw the mice and wouldn't put their trunks over them so the brick barrier was finished in no time! But nobody really knows if this was because the elephants didn't want to hurt the mice. You see, there is an old saying that claims "elephants are *frightened* of mice"!

Baby love?

A mum in Tanzania placed her baby on the ground under a tree while she worked. It was a hot day and there were lots of flies buzzing around. Suddenly a herd of elephants from the bush came along. They saw the baby and stopped. Two or three elephants pulled down branches from the tree. Then they gently and carefully covered the baby with them — they seemed to be protecting the human baby from the heat and the flies.

Did you know. . .?

1. Jumbo appetite

The African elephant eats up to 225 kg of grass, leaves and other vegetation every day – that's like a human eating 6,750 bowls of cereal a day. It drinks up to 136 litres of water in one go, which is like drinking 544 mugs of water. They spend up to 20 hours eating every day.

2. Tooth truth

Elephants go through six sets of teeth throughout their lives, because of the tough vegetation they eat. All African elephants have two tusks, which are special kinds of teeth which can grow up to three metres long.

3. All the better for hearing with?
An African elephant's ear is as big as a whole single bed. Unlike other animals, elephants don't have sweat glands for keeping cool. They use their enormous ear flaps for fanning cool air over their bodies.

4. Trunk calls
It's thought that elephants can recognize up to 150 other elephants by their calls. They communicate using deep rumbling sounds, which are too low for humans to hear.

5. That's handy!
An elephant's trunk is very muscular, and is almost as good as a human hand — an African elephant can use its trunk to turn

over the pages of a book, and it can pluck a single blade of grass from the ground. A trunk has lips like fingers which can gather food and water.

AIRMAIL FROM...

Would you like to read airmail letters from children in other parts of the world?

Airmail From South East Asia - *Ban Pong - where beetles taste great!* Shrimp writes to you from Thailand, about food, festivals, having fun Thai style, and lots more. Meet Frog, her brother (*not* her pet), and her funny Uncle Boon.

Airmail From Africa - *Ngorongoro - where cow poo is lucky!* Meet Christopher, a boy from Tanzania in Africa. He's dying to tell you all about his tribe, his four mums, and his *very* special cows.

AIRMAIL FROM...

Coming soon:

Airmail From South America –
Amazonia – where tree frogs go moo!
Maria and Leo are twins from
Copacabana in Brazil. They are going on
a brilliant adventure trip to the Amazon
Jungle, and they're writing to tell *you* all
about it.